RED TAYLOR S

PIANO
VOCAL
GUITAR

CW00435101

PUBLISHED BY
WISE PUBLICATIONS
14-15 BERNERS STREET, LONDON W1T 3LJ, UK.

EXCLUSIVE DISTRIBUTORS:
MUSIC SALES LIMITED
DISTRIBUTION CENTRE, NEWMARKET ROAD,
BURY ST EDMUNDS, SUFFOLK IP33 3YB, UK.
MUSIC SALES PTY LIMITED
UNITS 3-4, 17 WILLFOX STREET, CONDELL PARK, NSW 2200, AUSTRALIA.

ORDER NO. AM1006236
ISBN: 978-1-78038-939-4
THIS BOOK © COPYRIGHT 2012 WISE PUBLICATIONS,
A DIVISION OF MUSIC SALES LIMITED.

EDITED BY JENNI NOREY.
PRINTED IN THE EU.

WISE PUBLICATIONS
part of The Music Sales Group

London / New York / Paris / Sydney / Copenhagen / Berlin / Madrid / Hong Kong / Tokyo

STATE OF GRACE

Words & Music by Taylor Swift

2

never er _____ saw you __ com -

- ing. _____

And I'll nev - er _____

be the __ same. _____

pierce the room like a can-non-ball._ Now all we _ know _

_ is don't let _ go. _

We are a-lone,_ just you and me,_ up in your room _ and our

slates are clean, just twin fire _ signs, _

7

8

RED

Words & Music by Taylor Swift

Lov-ing him is like driv-ing a new Ma-ser-a-ti down a dead end street.

Fast-er than the wind, pas-sion-ate as sin, end-ing so sud-den-ly.

Lov-ing him is like

I still see it all in my head ____ in burn-ing ____ red. ____

____ Burn-ing, it was

red. _____

Oh, los-ing him was blue, ____ like I'd nev-er known. ____ Miss-ing him was

TREACHEROUS

Words & Music by Dan Wilson & Taylor Swift

25

I KNEW YOU WERE TROUBLE

Words & Music by Max Martin, Taylor Swift
& Shellback

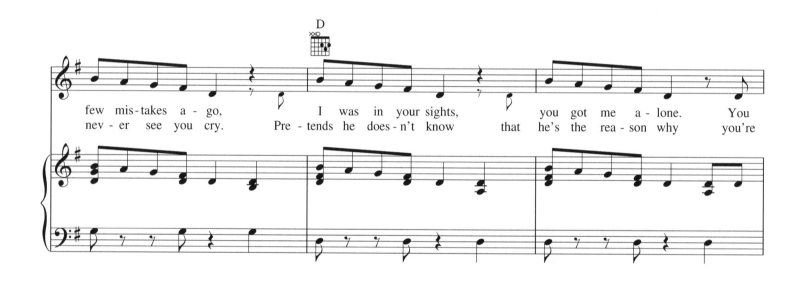

29

ALL TOO WELL

Words & Music by Taylor Swift & Liz Rose

22

Words & Music by Taylor Swift, Max Martin
& Shellback

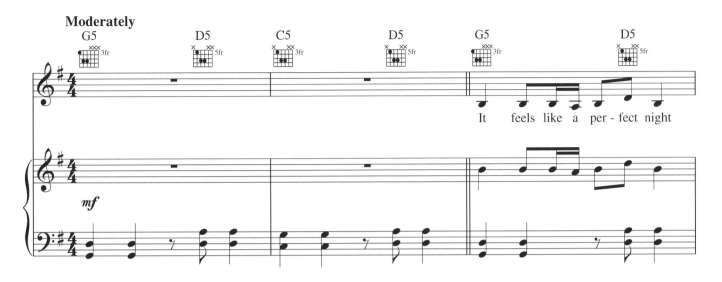

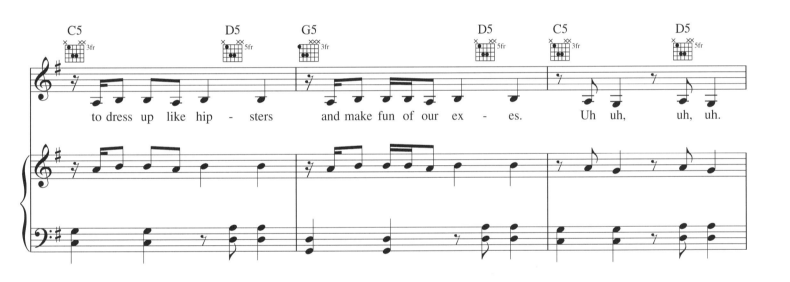

43

twen - ty - two, ____

twen - ty - two. ____

It seems like one of those nights. This place is too crowd - ed. Too man - y cool kids.

Uh uh, uh, uh. It seems like one of those nights we ditch the whole scene

we won't be sleep - ing. ___ It feels like one of those nights.

You look like bad news. I got - ta have you, ___ I got - ta have you. ___

Oh, ___ oh, ___

D.S. al Coda
(take 2nd ending)

N.C.

yeah, ___ yeah!

CODA

I got - ta have you. ___

I ALMOST DO

Words & Music by Taylor Swift

I bet you think I ei-ther moved on or hate___ you. 'Cause
each time you___ reach out,___ there's no___ re-ply.___
I bet it nev-er ev-er oc-curred to you___ that I can't say___ hel-lo___
___ to you and risk an-oth-er good - bye.___

CODA

al - most do, ____ I al - most do. ____

Oh, ____ we made quite a mess,

babe. It's prob - 'ly bet - ter off this way. And I con - fess, __

babe, in my dreams you're touch - ing my face and ask - ing me if I wan - na try a - gain with you.

And I al - most do. And I just wan - na tell _____ you

53

al - most do. _____

I bet this time of night you're still _____ up.

WE ARE NEVER EVER GETTING BACK TOGETHER

Words & Music by Max Martin, Taylor Swift
& Shellback

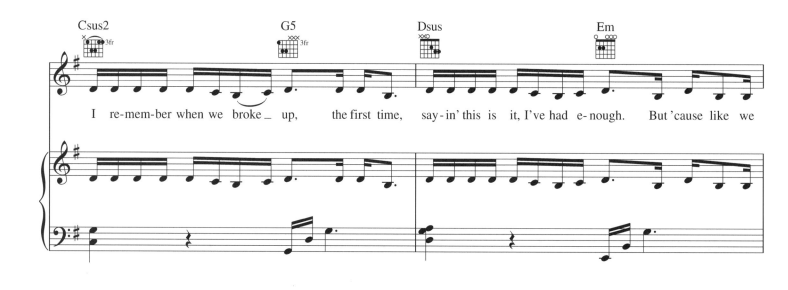

I re-mem-ber when we broke _ up, the first time, say-in' this is it, I've had e-nough. But 'cause like we

had-n't seen each oth-er in a month when you said you need-ed space. What?

STAY STAY STAY

Words & Music by Taylor Swift

THE LAST TIME

Words & Music by Gary Lightbody, Taylor Swift
& Garret Lee

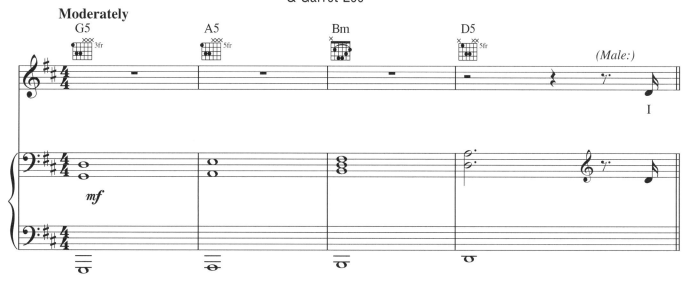

find my-self ___ at your door ___ just like all ___ those times ___ be - fore. ___

I'm not sure ___ how I got ___ there. All roads they lead me here. ___

70

last time I'm ask-ing you this. Put my name at the top of your list.

This is the last time I'm ask-ing you why you break my

heart in the blink of an eye, eye, eye.

74

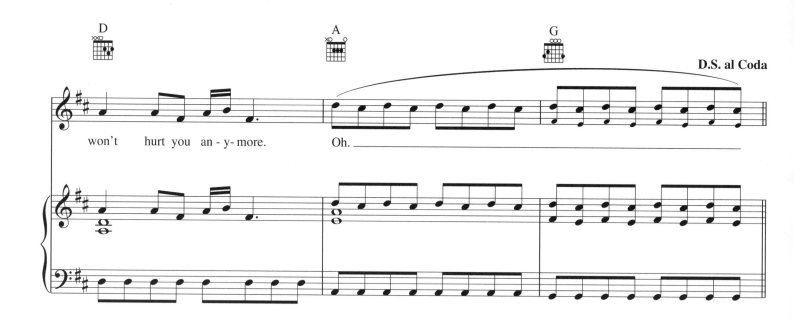

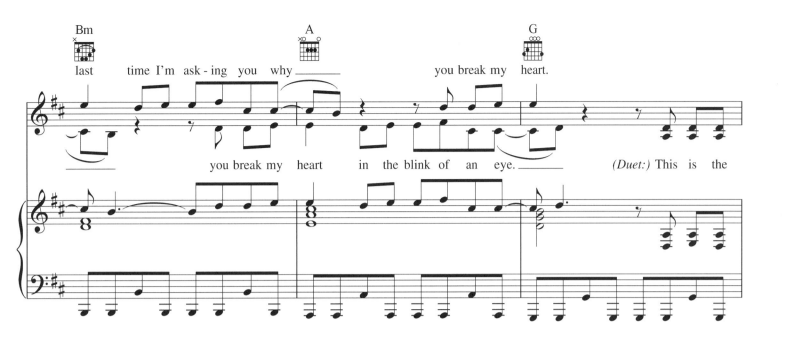

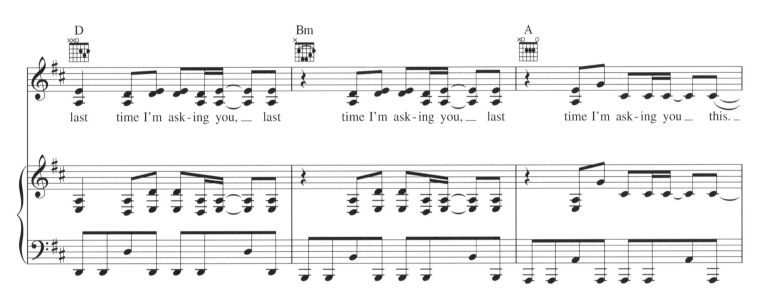

HOLY GROUND

Words & Music by Taylor Swift

nev - er look - ing down.

And right _____ there where we

stood was ho - ly ground. __

Spin-ning like a girl in a brand new dress, we had this big wide ci-ty all to our - selves. We block the noise with the sound of "I need you." And for the first time I had some-thin' to lose. And I

To - night I'm __ gon - na dance for all that we've been through. __ But I don't want to dance if I'm not danc - ing with you.

SAD BEAUTIFUL TRAGIC

Words & Music by Taylor Swift

* Sung an octave lower.

95

THE LUCKY ONE

Words & Music by Taylor Swift

EVERYTHING HAS CHANGED

Words & Music by Taylor Swift & Ed Sheeran

Recorded a half step lower.

STARLIGHT

Words & Music by Taylor Swift

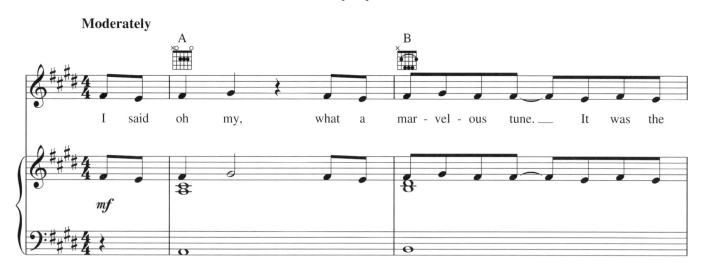

114

wor - ry - ing too much a - bout things you can't change. _____

You'll spend your whole life sing - ing the blues _ if you keep think - ing that way." _____

He was try'n' to skip rocks on the o - cean,

say - ing to me, _____ "Don't _ you see the star - light, star - light?

116

Oh my, what a mar-vel-ous tune. _ It was the best night. Nev-er would for - get how he moved. _ The

BEGIN AGAIN

Words & Music by Taylor Swift

Took a deep breath in the mir- ror.

He did- n't like it when I wore high heels, but I _____ do.

Turn the lock and put my head-phones on. He al-ways said he did-n't

get this song, but I _____ do, I _____ do.

Walked in ex-pect-ing
You say you nev-er met _____

And you throw your head ___ back, laugh - ing like a lit - tle kid. ___

I think it's strange that you think I'm fun - ny, 'cause he nev - er did. ___ And I've been spend - ing the last ___

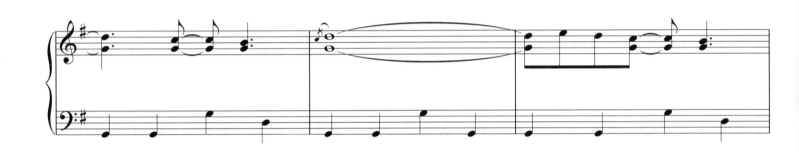

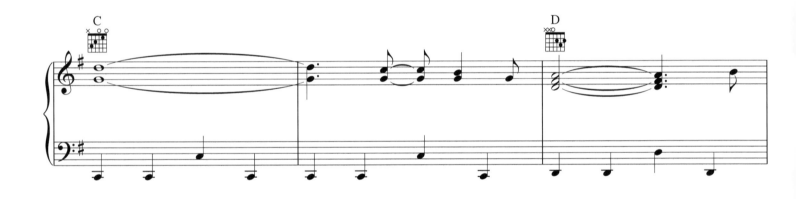

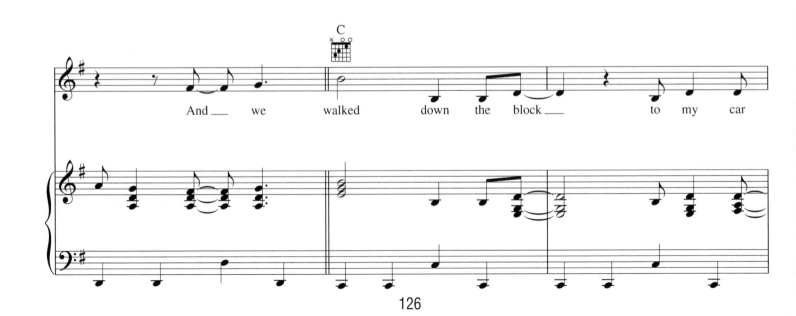

And — we walked down the block — to my car

and I al-most brought ___ him up, but you start to talk

a - bout the mov - ies that your fam - 'ly watch - es

ev - 'ry sin - gle Christ - mas and I want to talk a - bout that. ___

___ And for the first ___ time, what's past

3 4 5 6 7 8 9